HITS OF THE YEAR

UKULELE CHORD SONGBOOK

WISE PUBLICATIONS
part of The Music Sales Group
London / New York / Paris / Sydney / Copenhagen /
Berlin / Madrid / Hong Kong / Tokyo

Published by
Wise Publications
14-15 Berners Street, London W1T 3LJ, UK.

Exclusive Distributors:

Music Sales Limited
Distribution Centre, Newmarket Road,
Bury St Edmunds, Suffolk IP33 3YB, UK.

Music Sales Pty Limited
4th floor, Lisgar House, 30-32 Carrington Street,
Sydney, NSW 2000, Australia.

Order No. AM1011274
ISBN: 978-1-78558-188-5
Wise Publications,
a division of Music Sales Limited.

Compiled and edited by Adrian Hopkins.
Cover design by Tim Field.
Printed in the EU.

Your Guarantee of Quality:

As publishers, we strive to produce every book
to the highest commercial standards.

This book has been carefully designed to minimise awkward
page turns and to make playing from it a real pleasure.

Particular care has been given to specifying acid-free,
neutral-sized paper made from pulps which have not been
elemental chlorine bleached. This pulp is from farmed sustainable
forests and was produced with special regard for the environment.

Throughout, the printing and binding have been planned to ensure
a sturdy, attractive publication which should give years of enjoyment.

If your copy fails to meet our high standards,
please inform us and we will gladly replace it.

www.musicsales.com

Bills

Words & Music by Jacob Hindlin, Eric Frederic,
Rickard Goransson & Gamal Lewis

Intro

| G7(♭9) C11 | F B♭ | G7(♭9) C11 | F B♭ |

| G7(♭9) C11 | F B♭ | G7(♭9) C11 | C11 ‖

Chorus 1

(C11) F   B♭ C A   Dm
I got bills   I gotta pay,

    Dm9   C   F F/G C B♭
So I'm gon' work, work, work every day.

F C11 F   B♭ C A   Dm
I   got mouths   I gotta feed,

    Dm9   C   F F/G C N.C.
So I'm gon' make sure every - body eats.

    (F)
I got bills.

Verse 1

F   B♭   C   F   B♭   C
All these bills pile up my desk, they looking like a mount (Everest),

F   B♭   C   B♭   F C7/G
All the little kids run a - round, I can hear their stomachs growl.

F   B♭   C   F   B♭   C
It's a full moon out and my girl just keep on howlin',

F   B♭
She said she gonna leave me

C   B♭ F   C7/G
If I don't come home with fifty thousand.

Bridge 1

G7(♭9) C11   F   B♭
          God damn, God damn, God damn, God damn.

G7(♭9) C11   F   B♭
          Oh man, oh man, oh man, oh man.

G7(♭9) C11   F   B♭   G7(♭9) C11
          God damn, oh man, God damn, oh man.

Chorus 2

(C11) F   B♭   C   A   Dm
I got bills   I gotta pay,

     Dm9   C   F   F/G C   B♭
So I'm gon' work, work, work every day.

F   C11 F   B♭   C   A   Dm
I   got mouths   I gotta feed,

     Dm9   C   F   F/G C   B♭
So I'm gon' make sure every - body eats.

F   C11 (F)
I   got bills.

Verse 2

F   B♭   C
     Woke up and I bumped my head,

F   B♭   C
Stubbed my toe on the edge of the bed,

F   B♭   C
Opened the fridge and the food all gone,

               B♭   F   C7/G
Neighbour damn dog had crapped on my lawn.

F   B♭   C
Hopped in the car and the car won't start,

    F   B♭   C
It's too damn hot but I still gotta walk,

    F   B♭   C
Be - hind an old lady in the grocery line,

          B♭   F   C7/G
Praying that my card don't get de - clined.

Bridge 2   As Bridge 1

Chorus 3

(C11) F   B♭   C   A   Dm
I got bills   I gotta pay,

     Dm9   C   F   F/G C   B♭
So I'm gon' work, work, work every day.

F   C11 F   B♭   C   A   Dm
I   got mouths   I gotta feed,

     Dm9   C   F   F/G C   B♭
So I'm gon' make sure every - body eats.

Am   Gm
I   got.

Instrumental | F B♭ C | A   Dm Dm9 | C   F F/G | C B♭ F C11 |

| F B♭ C | A   Dm Dm9 | C   F F/G | C B♭ F C11 ‖

Bridge 3

G7(♭9) C11   F   B♭
       And my shoes,

G7(♭9) C11   F   B♭
        My shoes,

        G7(♭9) C11 F   B♭   G7(♭9) C11
I said my shoes   ain't got no sole._____

Chorus 4

(C11) F   B♭   C   A   Dm
I got bills   I gotta pay,

    Dm9   C   F   F/G   C   B♭
So I'm gon' work, work, work every day.

F   C11 F   B♭   C   A   Dm
I   got   mouths   I gotta feed,

    Dm9   C   F   F/G   C   N.C.
So I'm gon' make sure every - body eats.

Chorus 5

N.C. F   B♭   C   A   Dm
I got bills   I gotta pay,

    Dm9   C   F   F/G   C   B♭
So I'm gon' work, work, work every day.

F   C11 F   B♭   C   A   Dm
I   got   mouths   I gotta feed,

    Dm9   C   F   F/G   C   B♭
So I'm gon' make sure every - body eats.

Am Gm (F)
I   got   bills.

Outro

F   B♭   C A   Dm
   Mama got bills,   your daddy got bills,

     Dm9   F   Gm C   B♭   F
Your sister got bills,   your auntie got bills.

 C7/G F
I got   bills.

    F   B♭   C A   Dm   Dm9
Your uncle got bills,   everybody got bills,

C   F   Gm C B♭ F C7/G F
   Everybody got bills.

Blank Space

Words & Music by Max Martin, Taylor Swift & Shellback

| F | Dm | B♭ | C | Gm |

Intro | F   ‖

Verse 1
F
    Nice to meet you, where you been?
                           Dm
I could show you incredible things,

Magic, madness, heaven, sin.

Saw you there and I thought,
B♭
Oh my God, look at that face,

You look like my next mistake.
C
Love's a game, wanna play?

Verse 2
F
    New money, suit and tie,
                           Dm
I can read you like a maga - zine.

Ain't it funny, rumours fly
                           B♭
And I know you heard about me.

So hey, let's be friends,

I'm dying to see how this one ends.
C
Grab your passport and my hand,
N.C.
I can make the bad guys good for a weekend.

Pre-chorus 1   So, it's gonna be forever,

Or it's gonna go down in flames.

Dm
    You can tell me when it's over,

If the high was worth the pain.

Gm
    Got a long list of ex-lovers,

They'll tell you I'm insane.

B♭
    'Cause you know I love the players

                   F
And you love the game.

F

Chorus 1   'Cause we're young and we're reckless,

We'll take this way too far.

Dm
    It'll leave you breathless

Or with a nasty scar.

Gm
    Got a long list of ex-lovers,

They'll tell you I'm insane.

B♭
    But I've got a blank space, baby,

N.C.
And I'll write your name.

F

Verse 3   Cherry lips, crystal skies,

                       Dm
I could show you incredible things,

Stolen kisses, pretty lies,

                    B♭
You're the King, baby, I'm your Queen.

cont.   Find out what you want,

Be that girl for a month,
C
Wait, the worst is yet to come, oh no.

F
Verse 4   Screaming, crying, perfect storms,
                                         Dm
I can make all the tables turn.

Rose garden filled with thorns,

Keep you second guessing like,
B♭
Oh my God, who is she?

I get drunk on jealousy,
        C
But you'll come back each time you leave,
N.C.
'Cause, darling, I'm a nightmare dressed like a daydream.

Pre-chorus 2   As Pre-chorus 1

Chorus 2   As Chorus 1

N.C. (F)
Bridge   Boys only want love if it's torture,

Don't say I didn't say, I didn't warn ya.

Boys only want love if it's torture,

Don't say I didn't say, I didn't warn ya.

Pre-chorus 3   As Pre-chorus 1

Chorus 3   As Chorus 1

Outro   ‖: **F**   :‖ *Repeat and fade*

Blame It On Me

Words & Music by Joel Pott & George Ezra Barnett

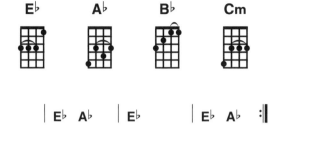

Intro ‖: E♭ | E♭ A♭ | E♭ | E♭ A♭ :‖

Verse 1

E♭
The garden was blessed by the gods of me and you,
                                                              B♭
We headed west for to find ourselves some truth, oh.
Cm   A♭   E♭ A♭ E♭ A♭
  What you waiting for, now what you waiting for?

Verse 2

        E♭
We counted all our reasons, excuses that we made,
                                                          B♭
We found ourselves some treasure and threw it all away, oh.
Cm   A♭   E♭ A♭
  What you waiting for, now what you waiting for?
Cm   A♭   B♭
  What you waiting for, now what you waiting for?

Chorus 1

B♭   A♭   E♭   B♭
When I dance a - lone and the sun's beating down, blame it on me.
                    A♭   E♭   B♭
When I lose con - trol and the veil's over - used, blame it on me.
Cm   A♭   E♭ A♭ E♭
  What you waiting for, now what you waiting for?

Verse 3

B♭   E♭
Caught in the tide of blossom, caught in the carnival,
                                                         B♭
Your confidence forgotten, I see the gypsies roll, oh.
Cm   A♭   E♭
  What you waiting for, now what you waiting for?
Cm   A♭   B♭
  What you waiting for, now what you waiting for?

Chorus 2

B♭   A♭   E♭   B♭

When I dance a - lone, and the sun's beating down, blame it on me.

                           A♭   E♭   B♭

When I lose con - trol and the veil's over - used, blame it on me.

Cm   A♭   E♭

What you waiting for, now what you waiting for?

Cm   A♭   B♭

What you waiting for, now what you waiting for?

Chorus 3

B♭   A♭   E♭   B♭

When I dance a - lone, and the sun's beating down, blame it on me.

                           A♭   E♭   B♭

When I lose con - trol and the veil's over - used, blame it on me.

                         A♭   E♭   B♭

When I dance a - lone, I know I'll go, blame it on me, oh.

                         A♭   E♭   B♭

When I lose con - trol, I know I'll go, blame it on me, oh.

Outro

Cm   A♭   E♭

What you waiting for, now what you waiting for?

Am   A♭   B♭

What you waiting for, now what you waiting for?

Blud

Words & Music by Bridie Monds-Watson

Intro | Fmaj⁹ | C | Fmaj⁹ G | C |

| Em | Am   ‖

Verse 1

Fmaj⁹   C   Fmaj⁹   C
You've got a problem, I cannot face it.

Fmaj⁹   C   Em   Am   G
Hear the anger through the ceiling,   I wish I missed it.

Fmaj⁹   C   Fmaj⁹   C   Em
Quit your em - ployment we can work with - out it___

        Am   G
If it means you are not sure for it.

Chorus 1

Dm   C   G
  You're in my blood,

Dm   C   G
  I'm in your blood.

Dm   C   G
  You're in my blood,

    Fmaj⁹   C   Dm
Oh,_____ let's just for - get,

    Fmaj⁹   C   Dm
Oh,_____ let's just for - get.

Verse 2

Fmaj⁹   **C**
Get up before they shoot you down,

Fmaj⁹   **C**
This is not worth the risk.

    Fmaj⁹   **C**
The shouting, dampened by the ceiling,

Em   **Am**   **G**
Oh, and I am waiting for what this is, oh, oh.

Chorus 2

Dm   **C**   **G**
  You're in my blood,

Dm   **C**   **G**
  I'm in your blood.

Dm   **C**   **G**
  You're in my blood,

  Fmaj⁹   **C**   **Dm**
Oh,____ let's just for - get,

  Fmaj⁹   **C**
Oh,____ let's just for - get.

Can't Feel My Face

Words & Music by Savan Kotecha, Max Martin,
Peter Svensson, Ali Payami & Abel Tesfaye

G   F   Am

Intro | G | F | Am | Am ||

Verse 1

               G   F
And I know she'll be the death of me, at least we'll both be numb,
             Am
And she'll always get the best of me, the worst is yet to come.
            G   F
But at least we'll both be beautiful and stay forever young,
            Am
This I know, yeah, this I know.

Pre-chorus 1

(Am)   G   F
She told me, don't worry a - bout it,
            Am
She told me, don't worry no more.
            G   F
We both know we can't go with - out it,
            Am
She told me you'll never be alone, oh-oh, whoo.

Chorus 1

G   F
I can't feel my face when I'm with you,
       Am
But I love it, but I love it, oh.
G   F
I can't feel my face when I'm with you,
       Am
But I love it, but I love it, oh.

	G **F**

Verse 2
                G   **F**
And I know she'll be the death of me, at least we'll both be numb,

              Am
And she'll always get the best of me, the worst is yet to come.

              G   **F**
All the misery was necessary when we're deep in love,

              Am
Yes I know, yes I know, man, I know.

Pre-chorus 2   As Pre-chorus 1

Chorus 2   As Chorus 1

Chorus 3   As Chorus 1

Link | **G** | **F** | **Am** | **Am**   ‖

Pre-chorus 3   As Pre-chorus 1

Chorus 4   As Chorus 1

Chorus 5   As Chorus 1

Outro | **G** | **F** | **Am** | **Am**   ‖

Cheerleader

Words & Music by Clifton Dillon, Sly Dunbar,
Mark Antonio Bradford, Omar Samuel Pasely & Ryan Dillon

E   B   A

Intro | E | B A | E | B A |

| E | B A | E | B A ||

Verse 1
```
      (A)    E                B            A          E
When I need motivation,    my one so - lution is my queen,
                             B           A
'Cause she stays strong,    yeah, yeah.
           E                    B          A
She is always in my corner right there when I want her,
               E                       B                A
All these other girls are tempting, but I'm empty when you're gone
```

And they say,

Pre-chorus 1
```
        E        A        B              A
    Do you need me, do you think I'm pretty,
        E            A            B     A
Do I make you feel like cheating? I'm like no, not really 'cause
```

Chorus 1
```
      E    A         B          A
Oh, I think that I've found myself a cheerleader,
      E    A         B          A
   She is always right there when I need her.
      E    A         B          A
Oh, I think that I've found myself a cheerleader,
      E    A         B          A
   She is always right there when I need her.
```

Verse 2

```
(A) E              A        B              A
She walks like a model    she grants my wishes
        E         A      B        A
Like a genie in a bottle,    yeah, yeah.
                 E        A       B             A
'Cause I'm the wizard of love and I got the magic wand,
              E            A           B                A
All these other girls are tempting, but I'm empty when you're gone

And they say,
```

Pre-chorus 2   As Pre-chorus 1

Chorus 2   As Chorus 1

Instrumental

```
| E  A   | B  A   | E  A   | B  A   |

| E  A   | B  A   | E  A   | B  A   |

| E      | B  A   | E      | B  A   |

| E      | B  A   | E      | B  A   ‖
```

Verse 3

```
(A)           E         A    B          A
She gives me love and af - fection, baby, did I mention
E            A            B            A
You're the only girl for me, no, I don't need a next one.
E            A            B                A
Mama loves you too, she thinks I made the right se - lection,
        E            A            B              A
Now all that's left to do is just for me to pop the question.
```

Chorus 3   As Chorus 1

Outro

```
| E  A   | B  A   | E  A   | B  A   |

| E  A   | B  A   | E  A   | B  A   |

| E      | B  A   ‖
```

Cool For The Summer

Words & Music by Savan Kotecha, Max Martin,
Alexander Kronlund, Demi Lovato & Ali Payami

Intro | (N.C.) | A♭ | Fm | Cm | Cm E♭   ‖

Verse 1

A♭maj7   Fm
Tell me what you want, what you like it's okay,
Cm
I'm a little curious too.
A♭maj7   Fm
Tell me if it's wrong, if it's right I don't care
Cm   E♭
I can keep a secret, can you?

Pre chorus 1

        A♭maj7   Fm
Got my mind on your body and your body on my mind,
        Cm   E♭
Got a taste for the cherry, I just need to take a bite.
A♭maj7   Fm
  Don't tell your mother,   kiss one another,
Cm   E♭   Cm
  Die for each other, we're cool for the summer. Ha!

Chorus 1

Cm   A♭maj7   Fm
Ooh, ooh, Take me down into your paradise,
Cm   B♭6   A♭maj7
  Don't be scared 'cause I'm your body type,_____
        Fm
Just something that we wanna try,
Cm   B♭6   N.C.
  'Cause you and I we're cool for the summer.

Verse 2

A♭maj⁷　　　　　　　　Fm
Tell me if I won, if I did, what's my prize?

Cm　　　　　　　　　　E♭
I just wanna play with you, too.

A♭maj⁷　　　　　　　　Fm
Even if they judge, fuck it, I'll do the time,

N.C.　　　　　　　　　Cm　　E♭
I just wanna have some fun＿ with you.

Pre chorus 2　　As Pre Chorus 1

Chorus 2

Cm　　　A♭maj⁷　Fm
Ooh, ooh, Take me down into your paradise,

Cm　　　　　　　　　　　　B♭6　　　A♭maj⁷
　Don't be scared 'cause I'm your body type,＿＿＿

　　　Fm
Just something that we wanna try,

Cm　　　　　　　　　　B♭6
　'Cause you and I we're cool for the summer.

A♭maj⁷　Fm
Ha!　　　We're cool for the summer,

Cm　　E♭
　We're cool for the summer.

Link 1　　| N.C.　　　| A♭　　　| Fm　　　| Cm　　　| Cm E♭　‖

Bridge

　　　A♭　　　　　　　　　　Fm　　　　　　Cm E♭
Got my mind on your body and your body on my mind,

　　　A♭　　　　　　　　Fm　　　　　Cm E♭
Got a taste for the cherry, I just need to take a bite.

N.C.
　Take me down!

Chorus 3

A♭maj⁷　Fm
Take me down into your paradise,

Cm　　　　　　　　　　　　B♭6　　　A♭maj⁷
　Don't be scared 'cause I'm your body type,＿＿＿

　　　Fm
Just something that we wanna try,

Cm　　　　　　　　　B♭6
　'Cause you and I we're cool for the summer.

19

Chorus 4

A♭maj⁷   Fm
Take me down,   we're cool for the summer,

Cm   B♭6   A♭maj⁷
Don't be scared 'cause I'm your body type,_____

     Fm
Just something that we wanna try,

Cm   B♭6
  'Cause you and I we're cool for the summer.

Cm
Ha! Ooh, we're cool for the summer.

FourFiveSeconds

Words & Music by Rihanna, Paul McCartney & Kanye West

Verse 1

           D   G   A   G
I think I've had enough,   I might get a little drunk.

           D   G   Bm A   D
I say what's on my mind,   I might do a little time.

           D   G   Bm   A
'Cause all of my kindness   is taken for weakness.

Chorus 1

           (G)   D   G
Now I'm four, five seconds from wildin',

                    D
And we got three more days till Friday.

                                       G
I'm just trying to make it back home by Monday morning,

           Bm   A
I swear I wish somebody would tell me ooh, that's all I want.

Verse 2

           D   G   D   G
Woke up an optimist,   sun was shining, I'm positive.

           D   G
Then I heard you was talking trash,

           D   G
Hold me back, I'm 'bout to spaz.

Chorus 2

   (G)   **D**   **G**
Yeah I'm 'bout four, five seconds from wildin',

                  D
And we got three more days till Friday.

                                   G
I'm trying to make it back home by Monday morning,

Bm   **A**
I swear I wish somebody would drive me,

Ooh, that's all I want.

Bridge

G   **F♯m**
  And I know_____ that you're out tonight,

Em
Thinking, how could I be so selfish?

G   **F♯m**   **Em**   **Bm**
  But you called 'bout a thousand times,

Asus⁴   **A**
  Wondering where I've been._____

G   **F♯m**
  Now, I know_____ that you're out tonight,

        Em
Thinking, how could I be so reckless?

G   **F♯m** **Em**   **Bm**
  But I just can't apolo - gise,

   Asus⁴   **A**
I hope you can under - stand.

Verse 3

D   **G**   **Bm**   **A**
  If I go to jail tonight,   promise you'll pay my bail.

D   **G**
  See they want to buy my pride,

Bm   **A**   **D**
  But that just ain't up for sale.

             G   **Bm**   **A**
See all of my kindness   is taken for weakness.

Chorus 3   As Chorus 1

Chorus 4   **D**   **G**

               Four, five seconds from wildin',

                        D

And we got three more days till Friday.

                                            G

Just trying to make it back home by Monday morning,

   Bm   **A**

I swear I wish somebody would tell me,

'Cause that's all I want.

Drag Me Down

Words & Music by John Ryan, Jamie Scott & Julian Bunetta

Cm   **A♭**   **B♭**   **Fm⁷**

Verse 1

    Cm   **A♭**
I've got fire for a heart,
                B♭
I'm not scared of the dark,
                 Fm⁷
You've never seen it look so easy.
  Cm   **A♭**
I got a river for a soul,
              B♭
And baby you're a boat,
            Fm⁷
Baby you're my only reason.

Verse 2

    Cm   **A♭**
If I didn't have you there would be nothing left,
   B♭   **Fm⁷**
The shell of a man who could never be his best.
    Cm   **A♭**
If I didn't have you, I'd never see the sun,
   B♭   **Fm⁷**
You taught me how to be someone, yeah.

Pre-chorus 1

  Cm   **A♭**
All my life   you stood by me,
B♭   **Fm⁷**
  When no one else was ever behind me.
Cm   **A♭**
All these lights,   they can't blind me,
B♭   **Fm⁷**   **(Cm)**
  With your love, no - body can drag me (down.)
Cm   **A♭**
All my life   you stood by me,
B♭   **Fm⁷**
  When no one else was ever behind me.

	Cm Ab
cont.	All these lights, they can't blind me,

B♭   **Fm⁷**   **Cm**
   With your love, no - body can drag me down.

          Cm A♭   **B♭**
Chorus 1   Nobody, no - body,

           Fm⁷   **Cm**   **A♭**
No - body can drag me   down.

                B♭
Nobody, no - body,

           Fm⁷   **Cm**
No - body can drag me down.

Verse 3   As Verse 1

Verse 4   As Verse 2

              Cm   **A♭**
Pre-chorus 2 All my life   you stood by me,

              B♭   **Fm⁷**
   When no one else was ever behind me.

              Cm   **A♭**
All these lights,   they can't blind me,

              B♭   **Fm⁷**   **Cm**
   With your love, no - body can drag me down.

          Cm A♭   **B♭**
Chorus 2   Nobody, no - body,

           Fm⁷   **Cm**   **A♭**
No - body can drag me   down.

                B♭
Nobody, no - body,

           Fm⁷
No - body can drag me.

Pre-chorus 3 As Pre-chorus 1

Chorus 3   As Chorus 1

Chorus 4   As Chorus 1

Elastic Heart

Words & Music by Sia Furler, Thomas Pentz, Abel Tesfaye & Andrew Swanson

Intro | D | A | E | F♯m   ‖

Verse 1

     D   A   E
And an - other one bites the dust,
  F♯m   D
Oh, why can I not conquer love?
        A   E
And I might have thought that we were one,
        F♯m   D
Wanted to fight this war without wea - pons.
        A   E
And I wanted it, I wanted it bad,____
    F♯m   D
But there were so many red flags.
          A   E
Now an - other one bites the dust,
    F♯m
Yeah, let's be clear, I'll trust no one.

Pre-chorus 1

    D   A   E F♯m
    You did not break me,
    D   A   E F♯m
    I'm still fighting for peace.____

Chorus 1

          D   A   E
Well, I've got thick skin and an elastic heart,
        F♯m
But your blade, it might be too sharp.
 D   A   E
I'm like a rubber band until you pull too hard,
        F♯m
Yeah, I may snap and I move fast.

cont.

```
            D                    A        E    F♯m
But you won't see me fall a - part,_____
            D                A            F♯m
'Cause I've got an e - lastic heart._____
```

Link 1

```
     D              A            E   F♯m
I've got an e - lastic heart,
            D                 A              E   F♯m
Yeah, I've got an e - lastic heart.
```

Verse 2

```
     D       A                                      E
   And I will stay up through the night,
        F♯m                          D
And let's be clear, won't close my eyes.
     A                      E
And I know that I can sur - vive,
        F♯m                          D
I'll walk through fire to save my life.
        A                                E
And I want it, I want my life so bad,___
        F♯m                     D
I'm doing everything I can.___
              A                        E
Then an - other one bites the dust,
        F♯m
It's hard to lose a chosen one.
```

Pre-chorus 2   As Pre-Chorus 1

Chorus 2   As Chorus 1

Bridge

```
     D              A                   E        F♯m
Oh, oh-oh-oh-oh, oh, oh, oh, oh, oh, oh-oh-oh-oh,
     D              A                   E        F♯m
Oh, oh-oh-oh-oh, oh, oh, oh, oh, oh, oh-oh-oh-oh,
```

Chorus 3   As Chorus 1

Chorus 4   As Chorus 1

Outro

```
     D          A    E
I've got an e - lastic heart.
```

27

Flashlight

Words & Music by Jason Moore, Sia Furler,
Sam Smith, Christian Guzman & Mario Mejia

Intro |‖ B♭ | C | F | B♭ ‖

Verse 1

B♭
When tomorrow comes I'll be on my own,
  C   F
  Feeling frightened of the things that I don't know.
                                   B♭
When tomorrow comes, tomorrow comes, tomorrow comes.
Dm
  And though the road is long, I look up to the sky,
C   F
  And in the dark I found, lost hope that I won't fly.
                        B♭
And I sing along, I sing a - long, and I sing along.

Chorus 1

  F
  I got all I need when I got you and I,
C   Dm
  I look around me and see a sweet life.____

I'm stuck in the dark but you're my flashlight,
B♭   F
  You're getting me, getting me through the night.____
                            C
Kickstart my heart when you shine it in my eyes,
                 Dm
Can't lie, it's a sweet life.

Stuck in the dark but you're my flashlight,
B♭
  You're getting me, getting me through the night.

Link 1

       F   C
'Cause you're my flash - light,

                Dm   B♭
You're my flash - light, you're my flash - light, oh.

Verse 2

      Dm
I see the shadows long beneath the mountain top,

   C   F
I'm not afraid when the rain won't stop,

                       B♭
'Cause you light the way, you light the way, you light the way.

Chorus 2   As Chorus 1

Bridge

  Dm   C   B♭
(Light, light, light, you're my flash - light)

                      C   Dm
Light, light, you're my flash - light.

                 C   B♭
Light, light, light, light, oh,___

You're my flash, oh.

Chorus 3   As Chorus 1

Link 2

  F   C
  'Cause you're my flash - light,

                    Dm
'Cause you're my flash - light,

            B♭
You're my flash - light.

F   C
Ooh, ooh, ooh, ooh,

Dm   B♭
Ooh,_____ oh, oh-oh.

Outro

  (B♭)   F
You're my flash - light, light, light,

                  C   Dm
You're my flash - light, light, light, yeah, yeah.

                              B♭
(Light, light, light, you're my flash - light, light, light.)

                 F
You're my flash - light.

High By The Beach

Words & Music by Lana Del Rey

Bm   G   Em   F#   D   A   D/F#   5fr

Intro

| Bm G | Em F# | Bm G | Em F# ||

Verse 1

Bm   G   Em   F#   Bm
 Boy, look at you, looking at me, I know you know how I feel,
     G   Em   F#   Bm
Loving you is hard, being here's harder,   you take the wheel.
     G   Em   F#   Bm
I don't wanna do this any - more,   it's so sur - real,
    G   Em   F#   (Bm)
I can't sur - vive if this is all that's real.

Chorus 1

Bm   G
All I wanna do is get high by the beach,
  Em   F#
Get high by the beach, get high.
Bm   G
All I wanna do is get by by the beach,
  Em   F#
Get by baby, baby, bye bye.
  Bm   G
The truth is I never bought into your bullshit
   Em   F#
When you would pay tribute to me 'cause I know that,
Bm   G
All I wanted to do was get high by the beach,
   Em   F#
Get high baby, baby, bye bye.

Verse 2

```
      Bm          G              Em   F♯                          Bm
      Boy, look at you looking at me, I know you don't under - stand,
                       G            Em       F♯                   Bm
      You could be a bad mother - fucker but that don't make you a man.
                          G              Em
      Now you're just an - other one of my problems,
           F♯                 Bm
      Be - cause you got out of hand,
           G        Em        F♯
      We won't sur - vive, we're sinking into the sand.
```

Chorus 2   As Chorus 1

Middle
```
      G                      D
      Lights, camera, acción;  I'll do it on my own,
      A                          Em              D/F♯
        Don't need your money, money to get me what I want.
      G                    D
      Lights, camera, acción;  I'll do it on my own,
      A                          Em              D/F♯
        Don't need your money, money to get me what I want.
```

Chorus 3   As Chorus 1

Bridge
```
      ‖: Bm  G   Em  F♯ Bm  G   Em  F♯ :‖
         High,_____    high,_____
```

Outro
(spoken)
```
      Bm            G          Em                  F♯
      Anyone can start again, not through love, but through revenge.
      Bm                  G
      Through the fire we're born again,
      Em              F♯           Bm
      Peace by vengeance brings the end. (High.___)
```

Hold Back The River

Words & Music by Iain Archer & James Bay

Em   D/F#   G   C   Dsus4   D   Am

Intro | Em D/F# | G | C G | G |

| C G | G | Dsus4 | D   ‖

Verse 1

Em   D/F# G   C   G
Tried to   keep you close to me,

G/B C   G   Dsus4 D
But life got in between.

Em   D/F# G   C   G
Tried to   square not be - ing there,

C   G   Dsus4   D
But think that I should've   been.

Chorus 1

C
Hold back the river, let me look in your eyes,

Hold back the river, so I

G
Can stop for a minute and see where you hide,

Hold back the river, hold back.

Link 1 | Em D/F# | G   ‖

<table>
<tr><td>Verse 2</td><td>

Em D/F♯ G   C   G
Once up - on a diffe - rent life,

    C   G   Dsus4 D
We rode our bikes into the sky.

    Em D/F♯ G   G   C   G
But now we're caught a - gainst the tide,

       C   G   Dsus4 D
Those dis - tant days all flashing by.

</td></tr>
</table>

<table>
<tr><td>Chorus 2</td><td>

C
Hold back the river, let me look in your eyes,

Hold back the river, so I

  G
Can stop for a minute and be by your side,

        D
Hold back the river, hold back.

C
Hold back the river, let me look in your eyes,

Hold back the river, so I

  G
Can stop for a minute and see where you hide,

        D
Hold back the river, hold back.

</td></tr>
</table>

<table>
<tr><td>Link 2</td><td>

Em D/F♯ G   C G
Oh, oh - ho, oh - ho, oh - oh,

    C   G   Dsus4 D
Oh - ho, oh - oh, ooh-oh, ooh-oh-oh.

</td></tr>
</table>

<table>
<tr><td>Bridge 1</td><td>

G
Lonely water, lonely water,

       C   **Am**
Won't you let us wander, let us hold each other.

G
Lonely water, lonely water,

       C   **Am**
Won't you let us wander, let us hold each other.

</td></tr>
</table>

Chorus 3

C
Hold back the river, let me look in your eyes,

Hold back the river, so I

   G
Can stop for a minute and be by your side,

      D
Hold back the river, hold back.

C
Hold back the river, let me look in your eyes,

Hold back the river, so I

   G
Can stop for a minute and be by your side,

      D
Hold back the river, hold.

Bridge 2

G
Lonely water, lonely water,

        C   Am   D
Won't you let us wander, let us hold each other.

G
Lonely water, lonely water,

        C   Am
Won't you let us wander, let us hold each other.

Outro

| Em D/F♯ | G | C G | G | |
| C G | G | Dsus4 | ‖ |

34

Hold My Hand

Words & Music by Ina Wroldsen, Jack Patterson, Jess Glynne & Janee Bennett

Intro | C | C |

Verse 1

C
Standing in a crowded room and I can't see your face.

(Oh-oh, oh, oh, oh, oh-oh-oh, oh, oh, oh, oh-oh-oh.)
Am⁷
Put your arms around me, tell me everything's okay.
C
(Oh-oh, oh, oh, oh, oh-oh-oh, oh, oh, oh, oh-oh-oh.)
Cmaj⁷
In my mind, I'm running round a cold and empty space.
Am⁷
(Oh-oh, oh, oh, oh, oh-oh-oh, oh, oh, oh, oh-oh-oh.)
C/F   C
Just put your arms around me, tell me everything's okay.
C
(Oh-oh, oh, oh, oh, oh-oh-oh, oh, oh, oh, oh-oh-oh.)

Pre-chorus 1

A♭maj⁷   F   C
Break my bones but you won't see me fall, oh.
A♭maj⁷   F   C
The rising tide will rise against them all, oh.

Chorus 1

(C)   **Cmaj7**
Darling, hold my hand,

                           Em7
Oh, won't you hold my hand?

                         F   **F/E**
'Cause I don't wanna walk on my own any - more,

                  Dm7
Won't you under - stand?

'Cause I don't wanna walk alone.

C   **Cmaj7**
I'm ready for this, there's no denying,

Am7
I'm ready for this, you stop me falling.

F   **F/E**
I'm ready for this, I need you all in,

Dm7   **F/G**
I'm ready for this, so darling, hold my hand.

Verse 2

C   **Cmaj7**
Soul is like a melting pot when you're not next to me,

          Am7
(Oh-oh, oh, oh, oh, oh-oh-oh, oh, oh, oh, oh-oh-oh.)

C/F   **C**
Tell me that you've got me and you're never gonna leave.

          C
(Oh-oh, oh, oh, oh, oh-oh-oh, oh, oh, oh, oh-oh-oh.)

                    Cmaj7
Trying to find a moment where I can find release.

          Am7
(Oh-oh, oh, oh, oh, oh-oh-oh, oh, oh, oh, oh-oh-oh.)

          C/F   **C**
Please tell me that you've got me and you're never gonna leave.

          C
(Oh-oh, oh, oh, oh, oh-oh-oh, oh, oh, oh, oh-oh-oh.)

Pre-chorus 2   As Pre-chorus 1

Chorus 2   As Chorus 1

Bridge

(F/G) **Fmaj7**   **Am7**
Don't wanna know that feeling when I'm all alone,

                              Fmaj7   **C**   **Dm7**
So please don't make me wait, 'cause I don't wanna break

        C   **G**
No I don't wanna fall.

                      Fmaj7   **Am7**
When you're next to me, can tell I'm not a - fraid to be,

                              Fmaj7   **C**   **Dm7**
That you don't make me wait and never let me break,

            C   **G**
You never let me fall.

Chorus 3

        (G)   **Cmaj7**
Darling, hold my hand,

                              Em7
Oh, won't you hold my hand?

                          Dm7   **Em7**
'Cause I don't wanna walk on my own any - more,

                              F
Won't you under - stand?

              N.C.
'Cause I don't wanna walk alone.

C   **Cmaj7**
   I'm ready for this, there's no denying,

Am7
   I'm ready for this, you stop me falling.

F   **F/E**
   I'm ready for this, I need you all in,

Dm7   **F/G**   **N.C. (C)**
   I'm ready for this, so darling, won't you hold my hand.

I Really Like You

Words & Music by Peter Svensson, Carly Rae Jepsen & Jacob Hindlin

Intro | B♭ | F | C   ‖

Verse 1
      Dm   B♭   F
I really wanna stop, but I just got the taste for it,
                   C
I feel like I could fly with the boy on the moon.
      Dm   B♭   F
So honey hold my hand, you like making me wait for it,
                  C   Dm
I feel like I could die walking up to the room, oh yeah.

Pre-chorus 1
B♭   F
Late night, watching television,
      C   Dm
But how'd we get in this po - sition?
     B♭   F   C
It's way too soon, I know this isn't love,
N.C.
But I need to tell you something.

Chorus 1
B♭   F   C
   I really, really, really, really, really, really like you
                                         Dm
And I want you. Do you want me, do you want me too?
B♭   F   C
   I really, really, really, really, really, really like you
                                         Dm
And I want you. Do you want me, do you want me too?
B♭   F   C
Oh, did I say too much? I'm so in my head when we're out of touch.
Dm B♭   F   C
   I really, really, really, really, really, really like you
                                         Dm
And I want you. Do you want me, do you want me too?

Verse 2

N.C.   B♭   F
It's like everything you say is a sweet reve - lation,

                 C
All I wanna do is get into your head.

     Dm   B♭   F
Yeah, we could stay a - lone, you and me, in this temp - tation,

              C   Dm
Sipping on your lips, hanging on by a thread, baby.

Pre-chorus 2   As Pre-chorus 1

Chorus 2   As Chorus 1

Bridge

B♭   F
   Who gave you eyes like that,   said you could keep them?

C   Dm
   I don't know how to act or if I should be leaving.

B♭   F
   I'm running out of time,   going out of my mind,

C   N.C.
   I need to tell you something,   yeah, I need to tell you something.

Chorus 3

N.C.   B♭   F   C
Yeah.___ I really, really, really, really, really, really like you

                                 Dm
And I want you. Do you want me, do you want me too?

B♭   F   C
   I really, really, really, really, really, really like you

                                 Dm
And I want you. Do you want me, do you want me too?

B♭   F   C
Oh, did I say too much? I'm so in my head when we're out of touch.

Dm B♭   F   C
   I really, really, really, really, really, really like you

                                 Dm
And I want you. Do you want me, do you want me too?

Chorus 4

B♭   F   C
Yeah. I really, really, really, really, really, really like you

                                 Dm
And I want you. Do you want me, do you want me too?

B♭   F   C
   I really, really, really, really, really, really like you

                                 Dm
And I want you. Do you want me, do you want me too?

Lava

Words & Music by James Ford Murphy

Intro | C | C | G7 | G7 | F | F |

| C | G7 | G7 ||

Verse 1
C   G7
 A long, long time ago there was a volcano
F   C   G7
 Living all alone in the middle of the sea.
C   G7
He sat high above his bay watching all the couples play,
F   C   G7
 And wishing that he had someone too.
C   G7
 And from his lava came this song of hope that he sang
   F   C   G7
Out loud every day for years and years.

Chorus 1
F   C
 I have a dream I hope will come true
   G7   C
That you're here with me and I'm here with you
 F   C
I wish that the earth, sea, the sky up above
   F G7   C F G7
Will send me someone to lava.

Verse 2

   C   G7
   Years of singing all alone turned his lava into stone

      F   C   G7
Un - til he was on the brink of extinc - tion,

   C   G7
   But little did he know that living in the sea below

      F   C   G7
A - nother volcano was listening to his song.

   C   G7
   Everyday she heard his tune her lava grew and grew

      F   C   G7
Be - cause she believed his song was meant for her,

   C   G7
   Now she was so ready to meet him above the sea

      F   C   G7
As he sang his song of hope for the last time.

Chorus 2

      F   C
   I have a dream I hope will come true

     G7   C
That you're here with me and I'm here with you

     F   C
I wish that the earth, sea, the sky up above

     F   G7   C
Will send me someone to lava.

Verse 2

   C   G7
   Rising from the sea below stood a lovely volcano

   F   C   G7
Looking all around but she could not see him.

    C   G7
He tried to sing to let her know that she was not there alone

      F   C   G7
But with no lava his song was all gone.

    C   G7
He filled the sea with his tears and watched his dreams disappear

      F   C   G7
As she remembered what his song meant to her.

Chorus 3   As Chorus 2

Verse 3

     C   G7
Oh, they were so happy to finally meet above the sea

F   C   G7
All together now their lava grew and grew.

     C   G7
No longer are they all alone with A - loha as their new home,

F   C   G7
And when you visit them this is what they sing:

Chorus 3

     F   C
I have a dream I hope will come true

      G7   C
That you'll grow old with me and I'll grow old with you

   F   C
We thank the earth, sea, the sky we thank too.

F G7 C
I   lava you,

F G7 C
I   lava you,

F G7 C
I   lava you.

Lips Are Movin'

Words & Music by Kevin Kadish & Meghan Trainor

Pre-chorus 1
G   Am   C
If your lips are moving, if your lips are moving,
               G
If your lips are moving, then you're lying, lying, lying, babe.
         Am   C
If your lips are moving, if your lips are moving,
              G
If your lips are moving then you're lying, lying, lying, babe.

Verse 1
G
Boy, look at me in my face,
Am
Tell me that you're not just about this bass.
C
  You really think I could be replaced?
G
Nah, I come from outer space.

And I'm a classy girl, I'm a hold it up,
    Am
You full of something but it ain't love.
    C
And what we got is straight overdue,
    G
Go find somebody new.

Bridge 1
     G
You can buy me diamond earrings
       Am   C   G
And de - ny-ny-ny, ny-ny-ny, de - ny-ny.

But I smell her on your collar
       Am   C   G
So good - bye-bye-bye, bye-bye-bye.

Chorus 1

N.C.   G   Am
I know you're lying 'cause your lips are moving,
C   G
Tell me do you think I'm dumb?
                                Am
I might be young, but I ain't stupid,
C   G
Talking 'round in circles with your tongue.
                            Am
I gave you bass, you gave me sweet talk,
C   G
Saying how I'm your number one.

                                      Am
But I know you're lying 'cause your lips are moving,
C   G
Baby, don't you know I'm done.

Pre-chorus 2   As Pre-chorus 1

Verse 2

G   Am
Hey, baby, don't you bring them tears,
                C   G
'Cause it's   too late, too late, babe, oh.
                      Am
You only love me when you're here,
                C   G
You're so   two-faced, two-faced, babe, oh.

Bridge 2   As Bridge 1

Chorus 2   As Chorus 1

Pre-chorus 3   As Pre-chorus 1

Chorus 3

N.C.
I know you're lying 'cause your lips are moving,

Tell me do you think I'm dumb?
             G   **Am**
I might be young, but I ain't stupid,
C
Talking 'round in circles with your tongue.
             G   **Am**
I gave you bass, you gave me sweet talk,
C   **G**
Saying how I'm your number one.

                                       Am
But I know you're lying 'cause your lips are moving,
C   **N.C.**
Baby, don't you know I'm done.

Photograph

Words & Music by Ed Sheeran & John McDaid

Intro

| E | E | C#m | C#m |
| B | B | A | A |

Verse 1

N.C.   E   C#m
Loving can hurt, loving can hurt sometimes,
             B   A
But it's the only thing that I know.
                  E   C#m
And when it gets hard, you know it can get hard sometimes,
             B   A
It is the only thing that makes us feel alive.____

Pre-chorus 1

C#m   A
    We keep this love in a photo - graph,
E   B
    We made these memories for ourselves.
         C#m   A
Where our eyes are never closing, hearts are never broken
       E   B
And times are forever frozen still.

Chorus 1

N.C.   E   B
So you can keep me inside the pocket of your ripped jeans,
                   C#m
Holding me closer till our eyes meet,
                A   E
You won't ever be a - lone, wait for me to come home.

Verse 2

N.C.   E   C#m
Loving can heal, loving can mend your soul
             B   A
And it's the only thing that I know, know.

cont.

                             E   **C♯m**

I swear it will get easier, remember that with every piece of you,

                   B   **A**

And it's the only thing we take with us when we die.

Pre-chorus 2   As Pre-chorus 1

             N.C.   **E**   **B**

Chorus 2   So you can keep me inside the pocket of your ripped jeans,

                                C♯m

Holding me closer till our eyes meet,

                        A

You won't ever be a - lone.

                      E   **B**

And if you hurt me, that's okay baby, only words bleed.

                              C♯m

Inside these pages you just hold me

                        A   **C♯m**

And I won't ever let you go, wait for me to come home,

                        A

Wait for me to come home,

                        E

Wait for me to come home,

                        B

Wait for me to come home, ooh.

             (B)   **E**   **B**

Chorus 3   You can fit me inside the necklace you got when you were sixteen,

                               C♯m

Next to your heartbeat where I should be,

                        A

Keep it deep within your soul.

                      E   **B**

And if you hurt me, well, that's okay baby, only words bleed,

                              C♯m

Inside these pages you just hold me

                        A

And I won't ever let you go.

             (A)   **E**   **B**

Chorus 4   And when I'm a - way, I will remember how you kissed me

                               C♯m

Under the lamp post back on Sixth Street,

                               A   **N.C.**

Hearing you whisper through the phone,   "Wait for me to come home."

Love Me Like You Do

Words & Music by Savan Kotecha, Max Martin, Ilya, Ali Payami & Tove Lo

A♭   Cm7   Fm7   D♭   E♭   E♭sus4

Intro
| A♭ | Cm7 | Fm7 | Fm7 |

| D♭ | E♭ | Fm7 | Fm7 ‖

Verse 1

(Fm7)   A♭
You're the light, you're the night,
          Cm7
You're the colour of my blood.
          Fm7
You're the cure, you're the pain,
                           D♭
You're the only thing I wanna touch.
        E♭   Fm7
Never knew that it could mean so much, so much.

Verse 2

(Fm7)   A♭
You're the fear, I don't care,
          Cm7
'Cause I've never been so high.
      Fm7
Follow me through the dark,
                       D♭
Let me take you past our satel - lites.
        E♭   Fm7
You can see the world you brought to life, to life.

Chorus 1

      A♭   Cm7
So, love me like you do, lo-lo-love me like you do,
Fm7   D♭
Love me like you do, lo-lo-love me like you do.
B♭m   Fm7
Touch me like you do, to-to-touch me like you do,
E♭sus4   E♭
What are you waiting for?

Verse 3

   (E♭)   **A♭**
Fading in, fading out,

       Cm7
On the edge of paradise.

      Fm7
Every inch of your skin

             D♭
Is a holy grail I've got to find.

   E♭   **Fm7**
Only you can set my heart on fire, on fire.

Bridge 1

  (Fm7)   **A♭**   **Cm7**
Yeah, I'll let you set the pace____

      Fm7
'Cause I'm not thinking straight,

  D♭   **E♭**   **Fm7**
My head's spinning around I can't see clear no more.

What are you waiting for?

Chorus 2   As Chorus 1

Chorus 3   As Chorus 1

Link | **A♭** | **Cm7** | **Fm7** | **Fm7**   ‖

Bridge 2   As Bridge 1

Chorus 4   As Chorus 1

Chorus 5   As Chorus 1

Outro | **A♭** | **Cm7** | **Fm7** | **Fm7**   ‖

Ship To Wreck

Words & Music by Florence Welch & Thomas Hull

Intro
‖: Am | F | Dm | Am :‖

Verse 1
    Am   F   Dm   Am
Don't touch the sleeping pills, they mess with my head,
              F   Dm   Am
Dredging the great white sharks,   swimming in the bed.
               F   Dm   Am
And here comes a killer whale   to sing me to sleep,
             F   Am
Thrashing the covers off, has me by its teeth.

Pre-chorus 1
        C   Dm   Am   F
And oh, my love remind me,   what was it that I said?
C   Dm   Am   F
I can't help but pull the earth around me,   to make my bed.
        C   Dm   Am   F
And oh, my love remind me,   what was it that I did?
        C   Dm
Did I drink too much, am I losing touch,
      Am   F
Did I build a ship to wreck?

Chorus 1
        Am   F   Dm   Am   F
To wreck,___ to wreck,___ to wreck,___
      Dm   Am
Did I build this ship to wreck?

Verse 2

```
Am                 F              Dm              Am
What's with the long face, or    do you want more?
                   F            Dm              Am
Thousands of red-eyed mice,    scratching at the door.
                   F
Don't let the curtain catch you,
Dm                                 Am
   'Cause you've been here be - fore,
                   F
The chair is an island darling,
Dm                      Am
   You can't touch the floor.
```

Pre-chorus 2   As Pre-chorus 1

Chorus 2   As Chorus 1

Interlude

```
Am    F       Dm     Am
   Ooh, oh, ooh, oh, ooh, oh.
      F      Dm       Am
Ooh, oh, ooh, oh, ooh, oh.
```

Bridge

```
(Am)      F         G                   Am
And good God, under starry skies we are lost,
      F
And into the breach we got tossed,
      G               Am
And the water's coming in    fast.
```

Pre-chorus 3   As Pre-chorus 1

Chorus 3

```
   Am   F   Dm   Am              F
To wreck,___ to wreck,___ to wreck,___
      Dm             Am
Did I build this ship to wreck?
   Am   F   Dm   Am              F
To wreck,___ to wreck,___ to wreck,___
      Dm             Am
Did I build this ship to wreck?
```

See You Again

Words & Music by Justin Franks, Cameron Thomaz, Charlie Puth & Andrew Cedar

Intro
| Gm   B♭ | E♭   B♭   F | Gm   B♭ | E♭   B♭ ‖

Verse 1

(B♭)   Gm B♭   E♭   B♭
It's been a long day with - out you, my friend,

         Gm   B♭   E♭   B♭
And I'll tell you all about it when I see you a - gain.

        F   Gm B♭   E♭   B♭
We've come a long way from where we be - gan,

F   Gm   B♭   E♭   B♭
Oh, I'll tell you all about it when I see you a - gain,

         E♭   B♭
When I see you a - gain.

Rap 1

Gm   B♭
    Damn, who knew?

F   E♭   B♭   F
    All the planes we flew, good things we've been through,

     Gm   B♭
That I'll be standing right here talking to you,

F   E♭   B♭   F
    'Bout an - other path, I know we loved to hit the road and laugh

Gm   B♭
    But something told me that it wouldn't last,

F   E♭   B♭   F
    Had to switch up look at things different, see the bigger picture.

Gm   B♭   F
    Those were the days, hard work forever pays,

E♭   B♭
    Now I see you in a better place.

Chorus 1

Gm B♭   E♭
    Ah. How can we not talk about family

B♭
When family's all that we got?

F Gm   B♭
    Everything I went through you were standing there by my side,

F   E♭   B♭
    And now you gon' be with me for the last ride.

Verse 2   As Verse 1

Link

N.C.   Gm B♭ F   E♭   B♭
Ah-ah, oh - oh, ah-ah, oh, oh-oh-oh-oh.

      F Gm B♭   F E♭   B♭
Ooh,＿＿ ooh,＿＿ ooh,＿＿ ooh, ooh.＿＿

Rap 2

Gm B♭ F   E♭   B♭
      First you both go out your way and the vibe is feeling strong,

F   Gm   B♭
And what's small turn to a friendship, a friendship turn to a bond.

F   E♭   B♭
And that bond will never be broken, the love will never get lost,

Gm B♭ F   E♭
    And when brotherhood come first,

        B♭
Then the line will never be crossed.

F   E♭   B♭
   Esta - blished it on our own, when that line had to be drawn,

F   E♭   B♭
And that line is what we reach, so re - member me when I'm gone.

Chorus 2

Gm B♭   E♭
    How can we not talk about family

B♭
When family's all that we got?

F Gm   B♭
    Everything I went through you were standing there by my side,

F   E♭   B♭
    And now you gon' be with me for the last ride.

Bridge

(B♭)   Cm7 B♭   Fsus4
So let the light guide your way, yeah,

Cm7   B♭   Fsus4
  Hold every memory as you go.

Gm   Cm7   B♭   F   Gm7 F   E♭(add9)
  And every road you take will al - ways lead you home, home.

Verse 3

(E♭(add9)) Gm B♭   E♭   B♭
It's been a long day with - out you, my friend,

        Gm   B♭   E♭   B♭
And I'll tell you all about it when I see you a - gain.

           Gm B♭   E♭   B♭
We've come a long way from where we be - gan,

F   Gm   B♭   E♭   B♭
Oh, I'll tell you all about it when I see you a - gain,

       E♭   B♭
When I see you a - gain.

Outro

(E♭(add9)) Gm B♭ F   E♭   B♭
Ah-ah,   oh - oh, ah-ah, oh, oh-oh-oh-oh.

     F Gm B♭   F E♭   B♭
Ooh,__ ooh,__ ooh,__ ooh, ooh.__

        Gm B♭ F   E♭   B♭
Ah-ah, oh - oh, ah-ah, oh, oh-oh-oh-oh.

     F Gm B♭   F E♭   B♭
Ooh,__ ooh,__ ooh,__ ooh, ooh.__

Shine

Words & Music by Gregory Kurstin & Olly Alexander

Intro   ‖: A   B | C♯m | B | B   G♯m :‖

Verse 1

```
     A                      B    C♯m
      I remember us a - lone,      waiting for the light to go.
     B                                            G♯m
      Don't you feel that hunger? I've got so many secrets to show.
     A                      B    C♯m
      When I saw you on that   stage,    I shiver with the look you gave.
     B                                            G♯m
      Don't you hear that rhythm, can you show me how we can escape?
```

Bridge 1

```
     A        B   C♯m              B
      Ooh, ooh, ooh, ooh, ooh, ooh, ooh, ooh.
                              G♯m     B
     I was biting my tongue, I was trying to hide.
              B   C♯m              B
     Ooh, ooh, ooh, ooh, ooh, ooh, ooh, ooh.
                         N.C.
     I'll forget what I've done, I will be redefined.
```

Pre-chorus 1

```
     A           B   C♯m               B
      It's shaking the sky and I'm following lightning,
              G♯m
     I'll recover if you keep me alive.
     A            B    C♯m                    B
      Don't leave me   be - hind, can you see me, I'm shining,
                  G♯m
     And it's you that I've been waiting to find.
```

```
                      A                  B   C♯m                           B
Chorus 1              I'm holding it all to - night, unfolding it all tonight.

                      You know that you make it shine,
                                         G♯m
                      It's you that I've been waiting to find.
                      A                  B   C♯m                           B
                      I'm holding it all to - night, unfolding it all tonight.

                      You know that you make it shine,
                                         G♯m              (A)
                      It's you that I've been waiting to find.


Link 1          | A      B | C♯m      | B           | B  G♯m    ‖

                      A                          B          C♯m
Verse 2               Now that we can hear that    sound,

                      Now that you can hold me down.
                      B                                         G♯m
                      You can pull me under, you can raise every - thing to the ground.
                      A                      B       C♯m
                      Everything I can ar - range,      every part of me you change.
                      B                                         G♯m
                      Just hold me together, tell me, you'll always want me to stay.


Bridge 2        As Bridge 1


Pre-chorus 2    As Pre-chorus 1


                      F♯m
Middle                Wanna be the one you steal,
                      C♯m                              B
                      I wanna be the one you shield,

                                                       A
                      I wanna be the one that your love,   that your love can heal.
                      F♯m
                      I wanna be the one you steal,
                      C♯m                              B
                      I wanna be the one you shield,

                                                       N.C.
                      I wanna be the one that your love,   that your love.
```

Link 2 ‖ A   B | C♯m | B | B G♯m ‖

Pre-chorus 3 As Pre-chorus 1

Chorus 3 As Chorus 1

Outro
A   B   C♯m   B
  Ooh, ooh, ooh, ooh, ooh, ooh, ooh, ooh.
                        G♯m   A
It's you that I've been waiting to find.____
          B   C♯m   B
Ooh, ooh, ooh, ooh, ooh, ooh, ooh, ooh.
                        G♯m
It's you that I've been waiting to find.

‖ A   B | C♯m | B | B G♯m |

‖ A   B | C♯m | B | B G♯m | C♯m   ‖

Uptown Funk!

Words & Music by Rudy Taylor, Robert Wilson, Lonnie Simmons,
Ronnie Wilson, Mark Ronson, Philip Lawrence, Jeffrey Bhasker,
Peter Hernandez, Charles Wilson, Nicholaus Williams & Devon Gallaspy

Dm7   **G7**

Intro

N.C.
Doh, do-do-do, do-do-do, do-doh.

                Dm7
Do-do-do, do-do-do, do-doh.

G7   **Dm7**
Do-do-do, do-do-do, do-doh.

G7
Do-do-do, do-doh.

Verse 1

N.C.
This hit, that ice cold, Michelle Pfeiffer, that white gold.

This one, for them hood girls, them good girls, straight masterpieces.

Stylin', wildin' livin' it up in the city.

Got Chucks on with Saint Laurent, gotta kiss myself I'm so pretty.

Bridge 1

       Dm7   **G7**
I'm too hot (hot damn), called a police and a fireman.

       Dm7   **G7**
I'm too hot (hot damn), make a dragon wanna retire, man.

       Dm7   **G7**
I'm too hot (hot damn), say my name you know who I am.

       Dm7   **G7**
I'm too hot (hot damn), am I bad 'bout that money, break it down.

Pre-chorus 1   Girls hit your hallelujah (whoo).

Girls hit your hallelujah (whoo).

Girls hit your hallelujah (whoo).

'Cause Up - town Funk gon' give it to you.

* = root notes only   **D***   **D♯***   **E***
'Cause Up - town Funk gon' give it to you.

F*   **F♯***   **G***   **G♯***
'Cause Up - town Funk gon' give it to you.

A*   **A♯***   **B***   **C***   **C♯***
Satur - day night and we're in the spot,

D*   **N.C.**
Don't   believe me, just watch. (Come on).

Dm⁷   **G⁷**   **Dm⁷**
Chorus 1   (Doh, do-do-do, do-do-do, do-doh.)

G⁷
Don't believe me, just watch.

Dm⁷   **G⁷**   **Dm⁷**
(Doh, do-do-do, do-do-do, do-doh.)

G⁷
Don't believe me, just watch.

N.C.
Don't believe me, just watch.

Don't believe me, just watch.

Don't believe me, just watch.

Hey, hey, hey, oh.

Dm⁷ N.C.
Verse 2   Stop,   wait a minute, fill my cup put some liquor in it.

Take a sip, sign a check, Julio, get the stretch.

Ride to Harlem, Hollywood, Jackson, Mississippi.

If we show up, we gonna show out smoother than a fresh jar o' Skippy.

Bridge 2   As Bridge 1

Chorus 2   As Chorus 1

Verse 3

Dm⁷
(Doh, do-do-do, do-do-do, do-doh.)

           G⁷
Before we leave,   let me tell y'all a lil' something.

Dm⁷   G⁷
Uptown Funk you up, Uptown Funk you up.

Dm⁷   G⁷
Uptown Funk you up, Uptown Funk you up, uh.

       Dm⁷   G⁷
I said Uptown Funk you up, Uptown Funk you up,

Dm⁷   G⁷
Uptown Funk you up, Uptown Funk you up.

Verse 4

(G⁷)   Dm⁷   G⁷
Come on, dance, jump on it, if you sexy then flaunt it.

       Dm⁷   G⁷
If you freaky then own it, don't brag about it, come show me.

       Dm⁷   G⁷
Come on, dance, jump on it, if you sexy then flaunt it.

       Dm⁷
Well it's Saturday night and we're in the spot,

G⁷
Don't believe me, just watch. (Come on).

Chorus 3   As Chorus 1

Outro

Dm⁷   G⁷
Uptown Funk you up, Uptown Funk you up.

Dm⁷   G⁷
Uptown Funk you up, Uptown Funk you up.

Dm⁷   G⁷
Uptown Funk you up, Uptown Funk you up.

Dm⁷   G⁷
Uptown Funk you up, Uptown Funk you up.

Dm⁷   G⁷
Uptown Funk you up, Uptown Funk you up.

Dm⁷   G⁷
Uptown Funk you up, Uptown Funk you up.

Dm⁷   G⁷
Uptown Funk you up, Uptown Funk you up.

Dm⁷
Uptown Funk you up.

Writing's On The Wall

Words & Music by James Napier & Sam Smith

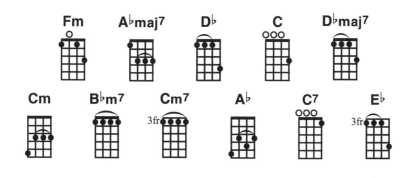

Intro | Fm | A♭maj7 | Fm | A♭maj7 |

Verse 1

Fm   A♭maj7
  I've been here be - fore

Fm   A♭maj7
  But always hit the floor.

    D♭   C
I've spent a lifetime running and I always get away,

    D♭   C
But with you I'm feeling something that makes me want to stay.

Verse 2

Fm   A♭maj7
  I'm prepared for this,

Fm   A♭maj7
  I never shoot to miss.

    D♭
But I feel like a storm is coming,

    C
If I'm gonna make it through the day

     D♭
Then there's no more use in running

    C
This is something I gotta face.

Chorus 1

Fm   A♭maj7   D♭maj7
   If I risk it   all

Fm   A♭   C7
   Could you break my fall?

        Fm   E♭
How do I live? How do I breathe?

            D♭   E♭
When you're not here I'm suffocat - ing.

       Fm   E♭
I want to feel love run through my blood,

     D♭   Cm
Tell me is this where I give it all up?

     B♭m7   Cm7   C7
For you, I have to risk it all,

N.C.   Fm   A♭maj7
   'Cause the writing's on the wall.

Verse 3

Fm   A♭maj7
   A million shards of glass

Fm   A♭maj7
   That haunt me from my past.

    D♭
As the stars begin to gather

     C
And the light begins to fade,

    D♭
When all hope begins to shatter

     C
Know that I won't be afraid.

Chorus 2

Fm   A♭maj7   D♭maj7
   If I risk it   all

Fm   A♭   C7
   Could you break my fall?

        Fm   E♭
How do I live? How do I breathe?

            D♭   E♭
When you're not here I'm suffocat - ing.

cont.

          Fm   **E♭**
I want to feel love run through my blood,

          D♭   **Cm**
Tell me is this where I give it all up?

        B♭m7   **Cm7** **C7**
For you, I have to risk it all,

N.C.   **Fm**
  'Cause the writing's on the wall.

A♭maj7   **Fm**   **A♭maj7**
  The writing's on the wall.

Link | **D♭** | **C** | **D♭** | **C**   ‖

Chorus 3

          Fm   **E♭**
How do I live? How do I breathe?

                D♭   **E♭**
When you're not here I'm suffocat - ing.

          Fm   **E♭**
I want to feel love run through my blood,

          D♭   **Cm**
Tell me is this where I give it all up?

          Fm   **E♭**
How do I live? How do I breathe?

                D♭   **E♭**
When you're not here I'm suffocat - ing.

          Fm   **E♭**
I want to feel love run through my blood,

          D♭   **Cm**
Tell me is this where I give it all up?

        B♭m7   **Cm7** **C7**
For you, I have to risk it all,

N.C.   **Fm**
  'Cause the writing's on the wall.

1 2 3 4 5 6 7 8 9

Whatever you want...

Music Sales publishes the very best in printed music for ukulele. Our books cover all levels of playing and all styles of music including rock & pop, jazz, blues and country.

Many of our practical publications come with helpful CDs or exclusive download links to music files for backing tracks and other audio extras.

We also publish a large variety of tuition books so you can teach yourself how to play, and ukulele resources for teachers.

So, whatever you want, Music Sales has it.

Just visit your local music shop and ask to see our huge range of music in print.

In case of difficulty, contact marketing@musicsales.co.uk